CONTENTS

GW00357502

Introduction
I.	**LEGISLATION**	2
II.	**TRAINING**	4
III.	**STABILITY**	6
	Centre of Gravity	6
	Stability Triangle	8
	Longitudinal Instability	8
	Lateral Instability	11
	Tip-over Procedure	13
IV.	**PRINCIPLES OF COUNTERBALANCE**	13
	Rated Capacity	15
	De-rating	16
V.	**FORKLIFT DO'S**	17
VI.	**FORKLIFT DON'TS**	26
VII.	**PRE-OPERATIONAL INSPECTION**	31
VIII.	**BATTERY MAINTENANCE PROCEDURES**	50
	Charging Area	57
IX.	**LOADS AND STORAGE**	60
X.	**GENERAL OPERATING PRACTICE**	64
	Parking and Travelling Positions	64
	Negotiating Inclines Unladen	65
	Negotiating Inclines Laden	66
	Loading and Unloading of Vehicles and use of Ramps	67
	Stacking Counterbalance	69
	De-stacking Counterbalance	72
	Stacking Reach Truck	75
	De-stacking Reach Truck	78
	Stacking Side-loader	80
	De-stacking Side-loader	83
	Stacking Pivot Steer Truck	85
	De-stacking Pivot Steer Truck	87
	Stacking Pedestrian Controlled Stacker	90
	De-stacking Pedestrian Controlled Stacker	92
	Picking Up Powered Pallet Truck	94
	Setting Down Powered Pallet Truck	96
	Stacking VNA	98
	De-stacking VNA	100
XI.	**LIFT TRUCK ATTACHMENTS**	102
XII.	**ADDITIONAL SAFETY RULES**	107
XIII.	**APPENDIX Safety Signs**	109

Introduction

Forklifts are extremely useful vehicles for loading/unloading loads as long as they are used safely and operators are fully trained and proved to be competent. Many developments took place during the mid nineteenth and early twentieth century that led to today's forklift design, but the modern forklift was developed in the 1920s by various companies. Since then it has become an indispensable piece of equipment in modern manufacturing and warehousing operations.

I.
LEGISLATION

Statutory Instrument 299 of 2007 (Safety, Health and Welfare at Work (General Application) Regulations 2007) applies, specifically regulations 34–42. The Regulations state the duties of the employer in respect of:

- Connection to energy source;
- Contact with wheels or tracks of mobile equipment;
- Drive systems of mobile work equipment;
- Combustion engines of mobile work equipment;
- Roll-over of mobile work equipment;
- Forklift trucks;
- Safety of self-propelled work equipment;
- Traffic rules for mobile work equipment.

The Safety, Health and Welfare at Work Act 2005 states that employees must be provided with **adequate** training. The HSA's *Code of Practice for Rider-Operated Lift Trucks: Operator Training and Supplementary Guidance and Retail and Distribution Sectors information pack* are useful documents that should be read by both lift truck operators and their managers. Forklift trucks must be examined, and the examination must be undertaken by a competent person once in every 12 months; this is a statutory requirement. Pre-operational inspections must also be undertaken (see page 31 and following pages).

Under the Safety, Health and Welfare at Work Act 2005 (Part 1, Sections 8–11) the employer's duties are as follows: *

- To ensure the safety, health and welfare of all employees whilst at work;
- To manage and conduct work activities in such a way as to ensure

the safety, health and welfare at work of all employees;

➡ To provide a safe, risk-free place of work, with safe means of access and egress, and to ensure plant and machinery are safe and do not pose a risk to health;

To ensure the safety of, and the prevention of risk arising from, the use of articles or substances or exposure to noise, vibration, etc;

➡ To provide systems of work that are planned, organised, performed, maintained and revised as appropriate so as to be safe and risk free;

➡ To provide and maintain facilities and arrangements for the welfare of employees at work;

➡ To provide information, instruction, training, and supervision as required;

➡ To implement the safety, health and welfare measures necessary for protection of employees as identified through risk assessments;

➡ To provide protective clothing and equipment where risks cannot be eliminated or adequately controlled;

➡ To prepare and revise emergency plans and procedures;

➡ To report accidents and dangerous occurrences to the relevant authority.

Employees also have duties under the 2005 Act (Part 2, Section 13); they are as follows: *

➡ **Duty of care to yourself.** Do not knowingly or deliberately put yourself at risk;

➡ **Duty of care to others.** Do not knowingly or deliberately endanger the safety of others through your acts or omissions;

➡ **Use all equipment correctly and safely.** Do not misuse, abuse, tamper with or modify any equipment provided for work. Where personal protective equipment is provided it must be used in accordance with instructions;

➡ **Co-operate with your employer** in all aspects of work concerning health and safety. This includes reporting to the management any incidents, accidents, near misses or faults to the equipment provided by the employer;

➡ **Attend workplace in condition fit for work.** Ensure that you are not under the influence of an intoxicant or suffering from an illness that could affect the health of others;

➡ **Attend training** and undergo such assessment as may be necessary;

➡ **Do not** engage in improper conduct or dangerous behaviour;

➡ **Comply** with all relevant statutory provisions;

➡ **Report to management** any work that might be undertaken in a dangerous manner or defects in the place of work or equipment etc;

➡ **Notify management of any illness or physical or mental impairment** that may affect your ability to undertake your job in a safe manner.

** A full list of the duties of both the employer and employee are available from the HSA website **www.hsa.ie**.*

II.

TRAINING

The Health and Safety Authority encourage the training of forklift truck operators in accordance with the HSA *Code of Practice for Rider-Operated Lift Trucks*

TRAINING QUESTIONS

Who Can Train Me?

Only qualified and registered instructors who have themselves undergone appropriate training in instructional techniques and skills assessment can train employees. Instructors should give instruction only on those type(s) of lift truck and attachments on which they have been trained and successfully tested as operators. Contact FÁS approved or RTITB/IIPMM accredited trainers.

Who Can Operate a Lift Truck?

Only employees who have been trained and tested, and have passed the basic training course should be considered as lift truck operators. Once basic training is completed, specific and 'familiarisation' training must be given before the employer can give the operator 'written authorisation'. **Only when the employee has completed all three stages of training and has received 'written authorisation' may he/she operate a lift truck.**

When Will I Need Further Training?

Refresher training should be undertaken at regular intervals to ensure the continued safe operation of the forklift. For specific information contact the accrediting body. Reassessment is especially essential where operators may not have used the lift truck for a period of time, or where there has been a previous accident or near miss, or if there is a change in working practices or the working environment.

TYPES OF TRAINING

Basic Training

Basic training covers the skills and knowledge required for the safe operation of a particular type of lift truck, as well as for carrying out routine pre-use inspections. Therefore, basic training may be given to novices and existing operators alike, although the training programmes and duration of training will vary.

Basic training should include the following elements:
- Introduction to the lift truck;
- Moving off and stopping;
- Basic steering operations;
- Manoeuvring in confined areas;
- Approaching, assessing, picking up, transporting and depositing loads;
- Various stacking and de-stacking exercises (free stacking, bulk stacking, metal corner post pallets and racking);
- Pre-use inspections;
- Refuelling procedures;
- Battery maintenance and charging;
- Lift truck stability;
- The safe use of hydraulics.

Specific Job Training

Specific job training will follow on from basic training. It should be tailored to the employer's special needs and will include, where appropriate:

Specific operating principles and controls of the lift truck being used, especially where the layout or use of the hand and foot controls differ from those on which the operator has been trained;
- Routine inspection and servicing of the truck in accordance with the operator's handbook, or instructions issued by the manufacturer, in so far as it is reasonable for the operator to carry them out;
- Use of the truck in conditions that the operator will meet on the job (e.g., the busy and changing environment of the workplace, slopes, uneven surfaces, gangways, lifts, racking systems, loading bays, load bearing structures, confined areas, cold stores and adverse operating conditions);
- Instructions on site rules (e.g., speed limits, site layout, one-way systems, use of protective clothing (including eye and hearing protection), emergency procedures, work near excavations, overhead lines and other hazards);
- Training in the work to be undertaken that may not have been included in basic training (e.g., loading particular vehicles and handling loads and materials of the type normally to be found in the workplace, including weight assessment and use of lifting attachments).

Familiarisation Training

Familiarisation training is the third stage of training, being the closely supervised element in which the operator first tackles 'live' work. It deals with the application, under normal working conditions, of the skills learned during the first two stages of training. It may be carried out by the trainee's supervisor, providing he or she has been suitably trained. Topics should include information on site layout, emergency procedures and any particular feature of the work which it is not practical to teach off the job.

III.
STABILITY

It is vital to understand the stability characteristics of a counterbalanced lift truck so as to avoid tipping over (see page 13), which can cause serious injury or damage to goods and/or structures. These characteristics are subject to the general principles of the centre of gravity and the particular effects created by the 'stability triangle', both of which are described in the following subsections.

Centre of Gravity

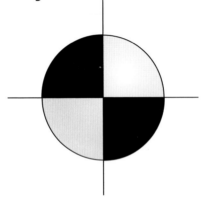

The centre of gravity is the balance point of an object (i.e. it is the point in the object where all the weight of the object is concentrated or the point at which all the surrounding weight is equal).

An object is unstable if its centre of gravity moves outside the points of support. The object will only remain stable if the centre of gravity (i.e. the point where all the weight of the object is concentrated) remains INSIDE the points of support.

The centre of gravity of an unladen counterbalanced lift truck is usually the point under and behind the operator's seat.

It is important to be aware that both the lift truck and the load it will carry possess their own centres of gravity. Only when the lift truck raises the load will the centres of gravity combine. The combined centre of gravity will be at a point somewhere between the two individual centres of gravity.

The truck and the load have their own individual centres of gravity

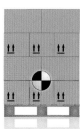

But as the load is lifted its centre of gravity and that of the fork truck shift to become a combined centre of gravity

Combined centre of gravity

Stability Triangle

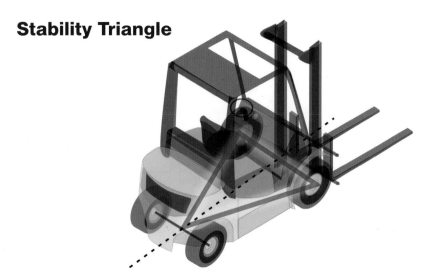

The body of a lift truck is carried on four wheels. However, it is the hinged rear axle that gives it the characteristic of a body carried on three wheels. The three-wheel characteristic creates the stability triangle.

This stability triangle dictates the centre of gravity of the lift truck. To understand the stability triangle, imagine a line running from the centre of one front wheel to the centre of the other front wheel and joining at the centre point of the rear axle.

To avoid tipping the lift truck over, the centre of gravity of the lift truck must remain inside the stability triangle at all times.

Longitudinal Instability

Lift trucks are usually counterbalanced. The pivot point ('fulcrum') is at the centre of the front wheel axle. To counterbalance is to balance one weight by another (e.g., the load carried by the lift truck is counterbalanced by the weight of the lift truck on the opposing side of the pivot point).

Longitudinal instability is the tipping forward which occurs when the load carried on the forks is too heavy. If the load is too heavy, the lift truck will be unable to counterbalance the weight of the load. In this case, the combined centre of gravity shifts outside the stability triangle (see page 9-10), causing a forward tip over.

Never pick a load up on the tips of the forks or with forward tilting forks as this will create the same effect as above (i.e. the lift truck will tip forward). Caution must be taken when driving down an incline as the centre of gravity may shift (i.e. the centre of gravity will move outside the stability triangle).

 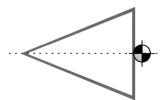

Travelling incorrectly on an incline (with a load)

 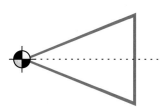

Travelling incorrectly on an incline (with forks raised)

 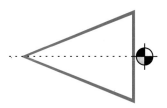

Tilting a raised load forward

 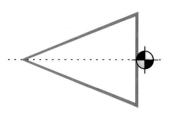

Lifting a load which is too heavy

 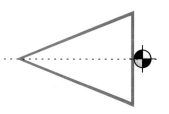

Harsh braking with a load

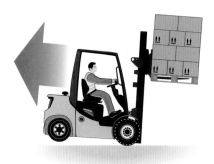 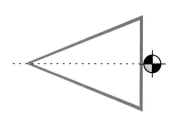

Reversing with a raised load

Lateral Instability

Lateral instability (i.e. tipping to one side) happens when the centre of gravity shifts to either side of the stability triangle. To prevent lateral instability, avoid driving across inclines and ensure the ground/floor is level and smooth. Lateral instability can also occur when corners are taken too sharply or too fast.

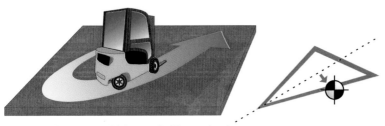

Making a sharp turn at high speed without a load

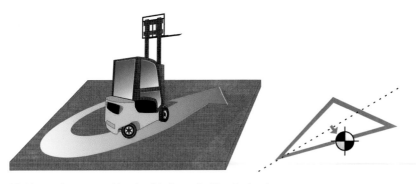

Making a sharp turn with raised forks and without a load

Making a sharp turn with raised forks and a load

III. STABILITY

 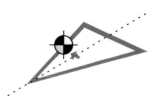

Travelling on uneven surface, soft surface (kerb etc)

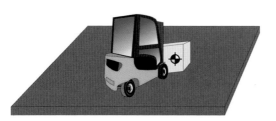 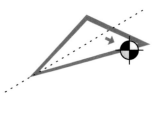

Travelling with a load off centre

 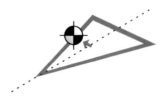

Traversing a slope

Tip-over Procedure
WHAT TO DO in the Event of TIP OVER

Plant your feet firmly on the floor panel and brace yourself by holding the steering wheel or overhead guard. Lean away from the direction that the forklift is tipping. Stay within the confines of the cab – Do Not Jump!!! Wear the seatbelt where fitted.

IV.
PRINCIPLES OF COUNTERBALANCE

The balance point of the forklift is the centre of the front wheel. In fact it can be compared to the principles of balance of a see-saw. From the diagram it is possible to see the weight of the load on one side is balanced by the weight of the body of the truck on the other. If the forklift is lifting within its capacity as stated on the rated capacity plate it will maintain balance; however, if the load on the forks is too heavy it will tip the forklift forward. As the operator you must be aware that as the load centre distance increases, the risk of a forward tip over will also increase.

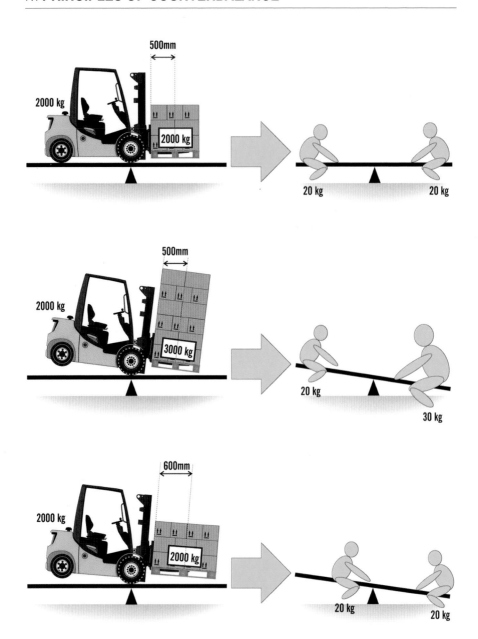

Rated Capacity

The rated capacity plate is attached to the lift truck at a point in view of the operator. It is a legal requirement to have the capacity plate fixed to the lift truck and it must be legible.

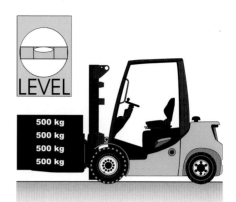

The rated capacity plate contains useful information (i.e. the maximum weight that the lift truck can lift, the height to which that weight can be safely lifted and the load centre distance). **The rated capacity plate is only applicable with the mast in the vertical position and the lift truck on flat, level ground.**

The information printed on a rated capacity plate only applies when the lift truck is on flat, level ground with the mast vertical and the fork-arms raised to the centre of the front wheel.

The load centre distance is a measurement from the vertical face of the fork-arm to the centre of gravity of the load. The carrying capacity is determined by the load centre distance. REMEMBER, as the load centre distance increases the carrying capacity will reduce.

If the actual load centre distance is less than that stated on the rated plate, you must not increase the weight of the load, as the stated weight is regarded as the lift trucks MAXIMUM capacity.

It is important to know the weight of your load before you lift it. Check the documents, or weigh the load. The weight of the load must not exceed the capacity indicated on the rated capacity plate.

When using attachments for unusual loads remember that the use of an attachment will change the lift-truck load capacity because of the increase in weight attributable to the attachment.

H3 – maximum height
D – load centre distance
Q – maximum capacity

h3 (mm)	Q (kg)		
4800	1500	1350	1220
4500	1550	1390	1260

D (mm)	500	600	700

Example of rated capacity plate

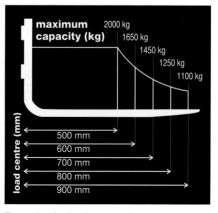

Example of a load centre plate

De-rating

When de-rating it is important to use the following formula:

Original rated capacity (1,600 kg) multiplied by the tested load centre distance (500 mm) divided by the new load centre distance (600 mm).

If the wide face of the load measures 1,200 mm and the narrow edge measures 1,000 mm, the load centre distance when entering on the wide face will be 500 mm and when entering on the narrow face the load centre distance will be 600 mm. So what can the lift truck raise when entering on the narrow face?

1,600 x 500 = 800,000 divided by 600 = 1,333.33 kg. Our rated capacity has now reduced to 1,333 kg.

DYNAMIC STABILITY

When a lift truck is not operating it should be stable. However, when a lift truck with a load is moving it may become unstable and dangerous because of dynamic forces that then occur. This dynamic stability includes longitudinal and lateral stability.

It is important to avoid sharp U-turns, even when the forks are not loaded. REMEMBER, the centre of gravity moves outside the stability triangle and the dynamic force of the turn will cause the lift truck to turn over.

The movement and position of the mast also play a role in dynamic stability. The centre of gravity will move forward as forward tilt is applied. Operating the lift truck with the mast in this position may result in a tip over because the centre of gravity may move out to the front of the stability triangle, especially at height.

Lowering the load prior to driving away ensures greater stability. Never attempt to raise the load so that you can see under it as this may cause a forward tip over and will restrict braking capacity because of the risk of tipping forward. If your view is obstructed by the load, drive in reverse or get a competent person to direct you.

STOPPING THE LIFT TRUCK

The lift truck has two small braking wheels.

When driving at a speed of 12kph the lift truck may take approximately 7-8 meters to come to a complete stop in the event of an emergency.

When driving at a speed of 6kph the lift truck may take approximately 3 meters to come to a complete stop in the event of an emergency. Operators should be aware that these distances can double when driving on wet, slippery, loose or icy surfaces.

When stopping suddenly with a heavy load there is a risk the lift truck could tip forward. Forward tip over can also occur when accelerating suddenly in reverse with a heavy load. Sudden starts and stops can cause the combined centre of gravity to move outside of the stability triangle.

LIFT TRUCK OPERATING AREA

Travelling up a gradient will cause the centre of gravity to move backwards in the stability triangle. When operating on an incline always keep the load on the **uphill** side. Never reverse up an incline with a laden lift truck as the centre of gravity shifts outside the stability triangle causing the lift truck to tip forward, and causing you to risk losing your load.

Do not drive with the load facing downhill or drive across an incline because of the risk of instability. Remember to drive directly up and down inclines.

Unsuitable ground surface may cause instability (e.g., potholes, uneven surfaces, kerbs, gravel and soft ground).

Remember to remove obstructions/debris out of your way rather than driving over them. Safely park the lift truck, dismount and move the object (s) to a safe area.

Specialised lift trucks should be used when working on soft ground such as mud.

V.
FORKLIFT DO'S

1. **ONLY operate the lift truck(s) that you have been trained, certified and authorised to operate.**
2. Always carry out a pre-operational inspection before starting work.
3. Report any accidents or near misses to your manager/supervisor.
4. Always report defects immediately and ensure an isolation tag is in place to prevent unauthorised start-up.
5. Ensure the truck is suitable for the work area.
6. Obey floor loading instructions.
7. Always face the lift truck when mounting and dismounting and use three points of contact.

8. Ensure the way is clear and where there are obstructions put them away in their appropriate place.

9. Obey all warning, mandatory, prohibition and information signs.

10. Carry out work environment hazard identification (i.e. risk assessment).

11. Assess the load before lifting: check the weight, size (load centre) and security of the load; ensure the pallet is in good condition; And check the load for additional information relating to the specific load handling requirements.

12. Use all controls smoothly to ensure maximum safety and stability of both the load and the lift truck.

13. Carry loads as close to the ground as possible. The fork-arms must be fully inserted when travelling with the load.

14. Lift the fork-arms approximately 6 inches (150mm) above the ground and apply a slight backward tilt when travelling without a load.

15. Always look in the direction of travel.

16. Always be aware of pedestrians when driving in or around pedestrian areas, because they may not be aware of you.

17. Wherever possible avoid operating the lift truck in areas where there are pedestrians. Remember that pedestrians have the right of way.

18. Ensure the load does not obstruct your view. If it does, drive in reverse, looking in the direction of travel.

19. Check the Safe Working Load (SWL) of racking. Racking should be able to sustain the weight of the load.

20. Observe speed restriction signs. If no signs are present the ground conditions will dictate the speed.

21. Take extra care when driving on wet, icy, slippery or loose surfaces.

22. Always keep a safe braking distance from any vehicle in front (recommended minimum separation distance of three lengths of your vehicle, although in special circumstances distances greater than three lengths may be required).

23. Take extra care when approaching blind corners, exits etc. SLOW DOWN and sound the horn **several times**.

24. Check pallets or stillages for damage before use.

25. Keep all body parts within the confines of the lift truck. If you need to lean out of the lift truck, first stop and secure the lift truck, then check all around for oncoming traffic and hazards, then hold on and lean out. (Do not hold the steering wheel).

26. Prevent anyone from standing on or walking under the fork-arms.

V. FORKLIFT DO'S

27. Always check the Safe Working Load (SWL) of lifts, ramps and road vehicles before you drive a lift truck on to or into them.

28. Ensure the bridge plates are able to sustain the weight of the truck and load, and that they are securely fixed.

29. Always drive over bridge plates slowly.

30. Ensure the mast of a lift truck will clear any overhead obstruction (e.g., roof/ceiling, doorways, lights, pipes and cables).

31. Approach the lift or road vehicle slowly and squarely.

32. Before driving an off-road vehicle, ensure the area is safe and the load is secure.

33. Ensure adequate ventilation is available when working in an enclosed environment.

34. Ensure fork-arms are lowered to the ground correctly. Make sure the power is off, keys removed and brakes applied before dismounting the truck.

35. Always park the truck in a safe area; do not obstruct doorways, footpaths, fire exits, first-aid stations or fire-fighting equipment, and if possible park on flat, level ground.

36. Always exercise caution when operating high lifts.

37. Operate the lift truck on smooth, level ground whenever possible.

38. Always cross kerbs, gullies, and railway lines slowly, at the designated points and diagonally.

39. If driving up an incline with a load that obstructs your view ensure a competent person is available to guide you.

40. When travelling with a load on an incline always have the load facing uphill.

41. When travelling on an incline without a load, drive with the forks facing downhill.
42. Ensure fork-arms are tilted backwards and raised sufficiently to clear the ground on an incline.

43. Always exercise extreme caution near overhead power lines.
44. Always ensure a safe distance is established between the truck and the edge of a platform, ramp etc.
45. Ensure fork-arms are correctly adjusted before collecting a load.
46. Ensure the fork-arms are secure and locked in place after you have adjusted the fork spread.
47. Ensure the load is firmly located against the backrest/heel of the fork-arm when travelling.
48. In cases where the load is not against the backrest/heel of the fork-arm, ensure the truck capacity rating allows for the increased load centre distance and ensure the load is sufficiently supported.
49. Always insert **both** fork-arms under the load before lifting it.
50. Always use extra caution when handling extra long, wide or high loads.

51. Before driving off, look out for other vehicles and pedestrians.

52. Look up before lifting to ensure that there is sufficient clearance. Be aware of overhead height restrictions.

53. Be aware of rear-end swing when cornering.

54. REMEMBER: minimum safe distance when following other lift trucks is three truck lengths.

55. In order to legally operate a fork truck on public roads it is necessary to possess a fork truck licence issued by a recognised and approved training provider, and a category W licence. A category W licence applies to work vehicles.

A 'Work Vehicle' is defined in the Road Traffic (Licensing of Drivers) Regulations 2006 as follows: a vehicle (other than a land tractor) which has a maximum design speed not exceeding 40km/h (see the above mentioned regulations for full definition).

Operators who are 16 years of age may apply for the W licence before applying for the category B licence (category B licence has a minimum age of 17 years).

It also necessary to ensure that the fork truck has all the relevant certification and insurance required by law and that the relevant, valid tax and insurance discs are displayed on the truck. Other certification may be required: for example, SAFE PASS is necessary when using a fork truck on a construction site.

The forklift truck must be registered and have number plates mounted at the front and rear which are not dirty and can be easily read.

If the truck can exceed a speed of 19km/h it must also be equipped with roadlights at the side, front and back to indicate stopping or direction. If the truck cannot exceed 19km/h such lighting is not obligatory so long as the driver can be easily seen on all sides, is able to make hand signals for the benefit of other traffic and does not use the truck after dusk except where adequate public lighting is provided. All forklift trucks must have number plate lights and all lights on vehicles must be the right colour, be clean and be working properly.

56. When operating in explosive or potentially explosive atmosphere use EX rated vehicle.

VI.
FORKLIFT DON'TS

1. Never use a lift truck that is defective. Always report defects immediately, and ensure an isolation tag is in place to prevent unauthorised start-up.

2. Do not use internal-combustion engine lift trucks indoors unless in conditions of adequate ventilation (risk assessment required). Turn off the engine and remove the key when not in use.

3. Do not carry unsecured loads higher than the fork carriage/backrest extension.

4. Never remove the backrest extension or overhead guard.

5. Do not fit or use attachments unless you are competent and authorised to do so.

6. Never drive over obstacles. Stop the lift truck, dismount and remove the object to a waste receptacle.

7. NEVER allow passengers on the lift truck unless a designated seat and seat belt are provided. Never carry a passenger on the forks.

8. Never tow or push other vehicles unless training and risk assessments have been completed.

9. Never lift unsecured or unsafe loads.

10. Never start or stop suddenly.

11. Do not make abrupt or quick turns.

12. Never turn with the load or forks elevated.

13. Never overload vehicles.

14. Ensure persons do not stand around unnecessarily when the truck is in operation. It is your duty to ask them to leave the area.

15. NEVER enter lifts, road vehicles etc without authorisation.

16. Never travel with the underside of a live load higher than 20 inches (500mm) from the ground, or with the mast tilted forward.

17. Never add counterweights to increase the load carrying capacity of the truck.

18. Never use two trucks to lift one load without first carrying out a risk assessment and completing a lifting plan.

19. Never leave a truck unattended on an incline. If absolutely necessary (i.e. in case of emergency) the truck may be left on an incline, but only with chocks at the wheels.

20. Never turn or drive across an incline.

21. Never raise the load above the travelling height on an incline.
22. Never approach within s̶i̶x̶ metres of an overhead power line.

ten

VI. **FORKLIFT DON'TS**

23. Do not place loose loads directly on to the ground.

24. Never stop the truck suddenly to offload the pallet/load. Deposit the load safely.

25. Never remove or alter safety devices.

26. Never smoke when refueling.

27. REMEMBER: minimum safe distance between lift trucks is three lengths of the lift trucks.

PRE-OPERATIONAL INSPECTION

PRE-USE CHECKLIST (DAILY)

Driver Name:		Date:	Time:
Fork Truck Make/Model/Reg Number:			
Item	N/A	Checked	Detected fault
Fork-arms			
Carriage Plate/Attachment			
Backrest Extension			
Mast			
Mast Rollers/Slides			
Lift Chains			
Chain Pulleys			
Hydraulics			
Wheels			
Tyres			
External Truck Body			
Battery			
Operating Position			
Capacity Rating Plate			
Operator Seat/Seat Belt			
Starting Procedure Electric Fork Truck			
Starting Procedure Engine Truck			
Starting Procedure			
Engine Truck			
Lights/Indicators/Flashing Beacon			
Audible Warnings			
Hydraulic Controls			
Driving/Braking			
Steering			
Other			
Faults Reported: ☐ Yes ☐ No Reported to:			Date

◄ Pre-use check sheet:
A pre-use inspection/check sheet should be completed and signed by the operator and manager in charge. The operator will need to inform the employer of any damage or wear to the lift truck. **If the lift truck is deemed to be dangerous DO NOT USE IT!**

➔ Fork-arms: *fork tips*
The tips of the fork-arms should be rounded with no sharpe edges. Check for thinning of the tips.

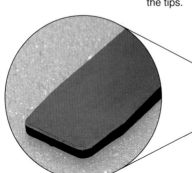

◄ **Fork-arms:** *arms*

Check the arms for scuffs and abrasions.
Ensure they are spread equally and not bent
or distorted.

◄ **Fork-arms:** *heels*

Check both the inside and underneath
of the heel for cracking.

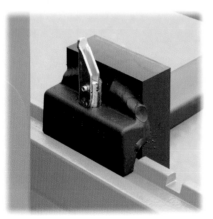

◄ **Fork-arms:** *retaining pins and hooks*

Check that the retaining pins are in
operation and keep the fork-arms locked
and secure. Check the weld area around the
hook for signs of cracking.

➡ Carriage plate:
Ensure the running gully is clear of debris
and lightly lubricated for ease of movement.
Check the carriage is square to the mast.

➡ Carriage plate:
Check the carriage is in good condition
and square to the mast.

⬅ Backrest extension:
Check to make sure the backrest is
connected to the carriage plate securely.
Check the weld areas are intact and the
backrest has not been damaged and/or
distorted.

← Stop bolts:

Ensure the stop bolts are in place and secure.

← Mast:

Check the outer sections of the mast for damage, distortion and cracks. Check the bracing bars and weld areas for damage. Check the fixing points/bolts to ensure the mast is attached securely to the body of the lift truck.

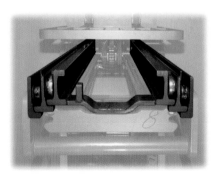

← Mast: *slides*

Check the mast slides are intact, secure, lubricated, clear of debris and without signs of scoring.

⬆ Mast: *rollers*

Ensure the rollers are attached and in good condition. Check the rollers for signs of uneven wear, incorrect tracking, flat spots and scoring.

⬆ Lift chains:

Check the lift chains for signs of loose or worn pins, damaged pin rivet heads and worn, cracked or missing links. Ensure the lift chain is lubricated. Check the tension of multiple chains to ensure that they share the weight of the load evenly.

⬅ Lift chains: *anchor points*

Check the chains are secured.
Also check for signs of damage.

◄ **Chain pulleys:**
Check for obvious damage, uneven wear and flat spots on the pulley system.
The chains should run over the pulleys and show signs of tracking correctly between the riveted end of the chain pins and inner walls of the pulley flanges.

◄ **Hydraulics:** *pipes and couplings*
Check the hoses for kinks, splits, cracks, tears and leaks. Ensure the hoses have not fouled in any part of the lift truck.
Check the couplings are intact with no signs of an oil leak.

◄ **Hydraulics:** *pistons/jacks*
Check the cylinders for any signs of external damage. Ensure all pistons are secure to the mast and anchored correctly. Check the seals for any signs of an oil leak.
The TAC hose reel (if fitted) should be undamaged and running freely with no sign of hydraulic leaks.

➔ **Hydraulics:**
Ensure all pistons are connected securely.

➔ **Hydraulics:**
Check the pistons are clean and have
a mirror like finish.

➔ **Wheels:**
Check to ensure all wheel nuts and bolts are
in place and secure. Examine the hub and
rim of the wheel for damage, cracks and
scoring. Check the inside of the wheel rim
for debris, banding, shrink wrap and other
foreign bodies.

➔ **Tyres:**
Check each tyre for excessive wear, tyre
wall deterioration, cuts and chunking.
Remove any nails, flints, stones, etc from
the tyre. Uneven tyre wear may be caused
by incorrect wheel alignment. Check the
tyres have equal pressure.

⊟ **Operator's overhead guard:**
Check each pillar for signs of damage or creasing. Ensure the roof and top of the mast are clear of loose objects. The roof glass/perspex and all window panes should be clean.

⊟ **External body:**
Ensure all panels are intact and in good condition. If panels are damaged inspect behind the panel for further damage. Check the body work for rust and damage to hinges and locks.

⊟ **Lights:**
Check the lights to ensure they are fixed to the body of the lift truck correctly and that there is no loose or bare wiring. The glass of light coverings should be in good condition and clean of mud etc.

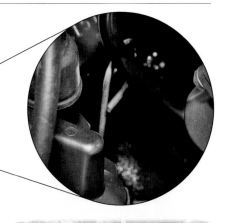

⊞ **Internal combustion engine:**
Check the oil and coolant levels are correct. When starting ensure the key and starter function correctly. Check the key stops the engine.

⊞ **LPG:**
The gas cylinder must be undamaged and mounted correctly with the locking pins or straps intact and secure.

⊟ **LPG:**
Check the supply pipe for kinks, damage, any signs of fouling and possible leaks. Turn the supply valves on and check for leaks. Check all seals, valves and couplings.

⊟ **Traction battery:**
Check the battery is secure and the power cable and plug also are intact and secure. Ensure the top of the battery is free from any liquid, debris or metallic objects. Check for signs of damaged or over-filled cells (generally caused by a build up of sulphur powder).

← Operator's position:

First check the rated capacity plate is located in view of the operator and pictorial decals are legible. Then ensure the footwell and area around the seat are clear of debris. Check the extinguisher is secure, charged and inspected (if fitted).

↑ Pedals and steering wheel:

Check the pedals have grip pads in place. Ensure there are no obstructions behind the pedals and that they can be depressed correctly. Ensure the steering is intact and fitted with a steering assistor.

↑ Operator's seat:

Check the seat is anchored to the body of the lift truck, the seat adjustment levers work and the padding of the seat is in satisfactory condition.

↑ Seat belt:

Check the seat belt for signs of damage, tears or cuts and for fraying of the stitching. Ensure the seat belt works as it should and the receiver holds the belt in place when it is in use.

⊡ Starting procedure:

Insert the key and turn on the lift truck. Check the display to ensure all relevant information is displayed. Checks should be made to any additional interlocks or gauges to ensure they are working in accordance with the manufacturer's operating manual. All motive power trucks apply.

⊡ Audible warnings:

Check the horn/claxon is working and is audible in your working environment. Checks must also be made to the reverse bleeper and handbrake warning indicators. It is imperative that the horn/claxon is working before the lift truck is moved or operated.

⊡ Lights:

Switch on all the lights including any indicator, reverse or brake lights.

⊡ Flashing beacon:

Turn on the flashing beacon to ensure it is working properly.

◄ Hydraulic levers:

Ensure all the levers are attached correctly and have the relevant decals in place.

◄ Multipilot:

Ensure the multipilot is attached correctly and in good condition with all relevant decals in place.

◄ Lift and lower lever:

Lift the fork-arms clear of the ground and bring the mast to the vertical position. As you lift the mast, stop and check the back of the carriage plate for any weld areas. Stop again when the heels of the fork-arms are just above your eye level so that you can check the underneath of the heels and fork hooks. Continue the lift to the full extension of the mast and check the pistons for signs of damage.

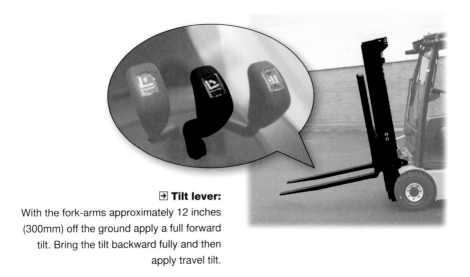

➔ Tilt lever:

With the fork-arms approximately 12 inches (300mm) off the ground apply a full forward tilt. Bring the tilt backward fully and then apply travel tilt.

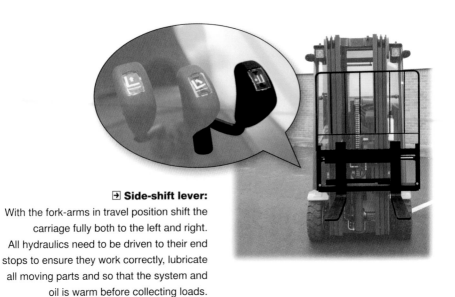

➔ Side-shift lever:

With the fork-arms in travel position shift the carriage fully both to the left and right. All hydraulics need to be driven to their end stops to ensure they work correctly, lubricate all moving parts and so that the system and oil is warm before collecting loads.

← Checking the brakes before moving the lift truck:

When checking the brakes ensure the handbrake is applied and press the footbrake checking for downward pressure. If the pedal goes to the floor there is a risk there may be a problem with the brakes. Repeat with the handbrake released comparing the amount of pressure in the brake pedal.

↓ Driving and braking:

Engage the reverse gear, check all around over both shoulders, release the parking brake and slowly move off checking the lift truck moves as it should. If there is enough room, accelerate and press the foot brake making sure the lift truck comes to a stop.

➡ Checking for leaks after having moved the lift truck:

Before checking in the forward direction, look on the floor where the lift truck was parked for any signs of leaks.
If there are puddles on the floor this could be any of the following:- hydraulic oil, engine oil, water or electrolyte.
If a leak is discovered, it will need to be reported to the management.

⬅ Checking both foot brake and parking brake are working adequately:

Engage the forward gear, check all around over both shoulders, release the parking brake and slowly move off checking the lift truck moves as it should. If there is enough room, accelerate and press the foot brake making sure the lift truck comes to a stop. Apply the parking brake and try to drive the lift truck checking for resistance.

If the lift truck moves without resistance the parking brake may not hold and the lift truck could move if parked on sloping ground.

Any brake issues must be reported immediately.

⬆ Steering:

With the lift truck moving slowly, apply both left and right turns in both forward and reverse directions ensuring the steering system works as it should.

If at any time a serious fault is detected, the fault report procedure must be followed.

Park the lift truck in a safe place.

Remove the key and isolate the lift truck.

Attach a sign informing others that there is a fault (tag out).

Report the fault to the management.

PRE-USE CHECKLIST (DAILY)

Driver Name:			Date:	Time:
Fork Truck Make/Model/Reg Number:				

Item	N/A	Checked	Detected fault
1. Fork-arms			
2. Carriage Plate/Attachment			
3. Backrest Extension			
4. Mast			
5. Mast Rollers/Slides			
6. Lift Chains			
7. Chain Pulleys			
8. Hydraulics			
9. Wheels			
10. Tyres			
11. External Truck Body			
12. Battery			
13. Operating Position			
14. Capacity Rating Plate			
15. Operator Seat/Seat Belt			
16. Starting Procedure Electric Fork Truck			
17. Starting Procedure Engine Truck			
18. Starting Procedure Gas Powered Truck			
19. Lights/Indicators/Flashing Beacon			
20. Audible Warnings			
21. Hydraulic Controls			
22. Driving/Braking			
23. Steering			
24. Other			
25. Other			

Faults Reported:	☐ Yes ☐ No	Reported to:	Date

PRE-USE CHECKLIST (WEEKLY)

Driver Name:				Date:				Time:		
Fork Truck Make/Model/Reg Number:										
Item	MON	TUE	WED	THUR	FRI	SAT	SUN	**Detected fault**		
1. Fork-arms										
2. Carriage Plate/Attachment										
3. Backrest Extension										
4. Mast										
5. Mast Rollers/Slides										
6. Lift Chains										
7. Chain Pulleys										
8. Hydraulics										
9. Wheels										
10. Tyres										
11. External Truck Body										
12. Battery										
13. Operating Position										
14. Capacity Rating Plate										
15. Operator Seat/Seat Belt										
16. Starting Procedure Electric Fork Truck										
17. Starting Procedure Engine Truck										
18. Starting Procedure Gas Powered Truck										
19. Lights/Indicators/Flashing Beacon										
20. Audible Warnings										
21. Hydraulic Controls										
22. Driving/Braking										
23. Steering										
24. Other										
25. Other										
Faults Reported: ☐ Yes ☐ No			**Reported to:**				**Date**			

VIII.
BATTERY MAINTENANCE PROCEDURES

Battery area requirements:
- ➜ Dedicated area for battery maintenance restricted to authorised personnel only (see page 57);
- ➜ Charger;
- ➜ Fire safety equipment (e.g., fire extinguishers (CO_2 or powder));
- ➜ First-aid equipment, including eye wash and first-aid shower or similar.

Personal protective equipment requirements:
- ➜ Full length PVC apron;
- ➜ PVC gauntlet gloves (long to cover majority of forearm);
- ➜ Full contact eye protection (goggles as minimum, full face mask recommended).

Correct Personal Protective Equipment

VIII. BATTERY MAINTENANCE PROCEDURES

Relevant equipment for checking and filling of battery:
- Torch to check levels (non-metallic, EX rated);
- Hydrometer to check specific gravity of electrolyte;

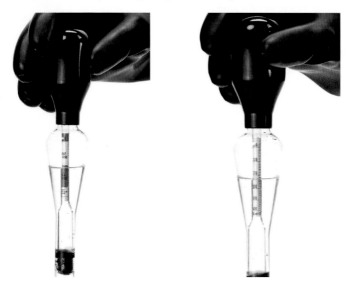

Specific Gravity Reading

- Battery log book to record checks and specific gravity readings;
- Funnel and jug for topping-up (non-metallic) or a measuring jug;

Measuring Jug (non-metallic)

▶ Distilled, de-ionised or pure water for topping-up;
▶ Cloth for cleaning battery tops (paper preferred) no nylon as can produce static;
▶ Bicarbonate of soda for any acid spillage.

Procedure for Manual Top-Up of Battery

1. Park the lift truck in the designated area for maintenance.
2. Put on the relevant personal protective equipment.
3. Open the battery cover.
4. Open a few battery caps at random to carry out a 'pilot check' (a pilot check is a check of the battery cells. All cells need to be checked within 28 days or by the seventh charge. Pilot checks will allow employees to alert the employer to the existence of damaged cells, thereby reducing costs of repair/ replacement).

**De-ionised
(distilled) water**

Pilot Check

VIII. BATTERY MAINTENANCE PROCEDURES

5. Using the hydrometer, test the specific gravity of the selected cells. Enter the results in the log book. Full charge reading will be 1.280 and a flat charge reading will be 1.140.

BATTERY MAINTENANCE (SPECIFIC GRAVITY) – RECORD FORM

Fork Truck – Serial Number:
....

Battery Serial Number:
....

Date of Test:
....

Cell number

Specific gravity before charging

1

Graphic representation of battery connections

Specific gravity after charging

1		**2**		**3**		**4**	
8		**7**		**6**		**5**	
9		**10**		**11**		**12**	
16		**15**		**14**		**13**	
17		**18**		**19**		**20**	
24		**23**		**22**		**21**	

All cells should be checked within 28 days or by the seventh charge.

Specific gravity: **1.280 FULL**   **1.140 FLAT**

6. When this process is complete rinse the hydrometer thoroughly thus reducing the risk of injury to personnel.

7. Open the remainder of the cells and using the torch check the cell levels (the level needs to be just above the lead plates within the cell. Overfilling can cause spillage when the battery is being charged). If the level is correct, close the cell, leaving the cells that need topping-up open.

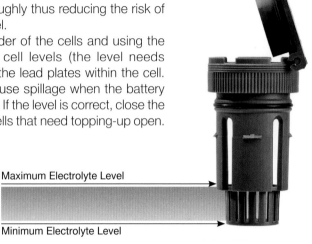

Maximum Electrolyte Level

Minimum Electrolyte Level

8. To avoid spillage, place the funnel into the cell and then pour distilled water with the jug into the cell until the level is just above the lead plates. Close the cell once you have topped up.

9. Using the paper cloth, wipe the battery top and dispose of the cloth in a contaminated-waste receptacle.

10. Ensure all cells are closed firmly so that the battery is ready for use.

11. Topping-up should only take place after the battery has been charged. This will reduce the risk of the electrolyte overflowing the top of the battery, which could damage the tops of the cells and cause corrosion.

Procedure for Auto-Fill of Battery

1. Park the lift truck in the designated area for maintenance.

2. Put on the relevant personal protective equipment.

3. Open the battery cover.

4. Open a few battery caps at random to carry out a 'pilot check' (a pilot check is a check of the battery cells. All cells need to be checked within 28 days or by the seventh charge. Pilot checks will allow employees to alert the employer to the existence of damaged cells, thereby reducing costs of repair/replacement).

5. Using the hydrometer, test the specific gravity of the selected cells. Enter the results in the log book. When this process is complete rinse the hydrometer thoroughly thus reducing the risk of injury to personnel.

6. Look at the level indicator to see if the battery requires topping-up: low indicator means it needs a top-up and high indicator that it does not.
7. Connect the hydro-caddy hose to the battery hose and switch the hydro-caddy on. Watch the spinning dial and as soon as it slows down switch the hydro-caddy off. If the hydro-caddy is left running the interconnecting hoses will start to leak water.
8. Disconnect the hydro-caddy.
9. Using the paper cloth wipe the battery top and dispose of the cloth in a contaminated-waste receptacle.
10. Ensure all cells are closed firmly so that the battery is ready for use.
11. Topping-up should only take place after the battery has been charged. This will reduce the risk of the electrolyte overflowing the top of the battery, which could damage the tops of the cells and cause corrosion.

Procedure for Charging the Battery

1. Park the lift truck in the designated battery area.
2. Expose the battery by lifting the battery lid or reaching the battery out (reach trucks).
3. Check the relevant charger leads and plugs are in good condition and that the power is OFF and the mains lead is DISCONNECTED.
4. Check the battery lead and plug are in good condition.
5. Connect the charger lead to the battery lead.
6. Plug in the charger mains plug into the mains socket and if there is a power switch, turn to the on position.
7. The charger will not start for a few seconds, allowing the operator to move to a safe position in which, should there be a fault in the charger, a shock will not be received.
8. Before leaving the charging area, make sure the charger has started.
9. The charging of a lift truck battery can take up to 12 hours.

Procedure for Disconnecting the Battery from the Charger

1. Check if the charger has completed the charging cycle.
2. If the charger is still charging, switch off at the mains only, allowing the gases to disperse. After about 5 to 10 minutes unplug the mains and tidy away the lead.
3. Disconnect the charger lead from the battery lead and tidy away the lead, so preventing trips, falls and damage to the lead or plug.
4. Check lift truck leads are in good condition and that no damage has occurred during the charging process.

5. Connect the battery lead to the lift truck.
6. Close the battery lid (reach battery into housing on a reach truck).
7. The lift truck is now ready for use.

DO NOT

➡ Smoke or bring naked flames in or around the battery charging area;
➡ Use metallic objects when working on or topping-up the battery;
➡ Place metallic objects or tools on top of the battery;
➡ Use a naked flame to check the levels of the battery;
➡ Overfill the cells of the battery;
➡ Leave the battery cells open when charging;
➡ Connect the leads when the mains power is ON;
➡ Eat or drink when working with batteries;
➡ Leave the battery to discharge completely.

ALWAYS

➡ Wear your personal protective equipment when working with batteries;
➡ Carry out battery maintenance in the designated area;
➡ Check the charger and leads before use;
➡ Ensure the lift truck is parked and secured correctly before starting the maintenance;
   Top up and charge the battery at regular intervals;
➡ Use distilled deionised or pure water to top up the battery;
➡ Fill battery to the correct levels;
➡ Expose the battery top when charging, allowing the gases to disperse;
➡ Hang up the leads when not in use;
➡ Report to your supervisor/manager if the battery has not completed its charging cycle by the start of your shift;
➡ Report any damage to the charger or battery;
➡ Tell your supervisor/manager if any battery cells have not charged correctly;
➡ Seek assistance when in doubt;
➡ Wash your hands after handling or touching batteries.

CHARGING AREA

Ensure the battery charging area is fully equipped and designated for battery care and maintenance ONLY

Only remove the battery when the lift truck is parked on level ground. Do not attempt to remove the battery from a laden lift truck. When changing batteries ensure the replacement battery is of the same size and weight as the battery to be replaced, as this can affect the stability and capacity of the lift truck.

Only specifically designed lifting equipment may be used when lifting the battery. Lifting equipment must be certified and only used by trained and competent personnel.

Rope slings and chain slings should not be used for lifting as they exert pressure on the battery when the sides of the battery case are pulled together during the lift. This action may cause the crushing of the battery cells. Always exercise caution when handling batteries. Care must be taken to prevent bumping a battery on the ground as this may cause the cells to secrete active material from the plates, and may cause a short circuit. The overall efficiency of the battery and the cell capacity may be reduced as a result of careless knocks.

Modern lift trucks are designed so that they do not require special lifting equipment; however, a pallet truck may be necessary.

Many makes and models of lift truck in the workplace will require special lifting equipment; always read the manufacturer's manual.

Hoist attachment points indicated on a battery.

IX.
LOADS AND STORAGE

Types of pallets

Two-way entry reversible
This pallet is fully boarded on both sides.

Pallet movers, low-level order pickers or support arm stackers are not suitable for this type of pallet

It can be lifted with rider operated counterbalance or reach forklift trucks (as only the forks are inserted). Straddle stackers can also be used as long as the support legs are on the outside of the pallet.

Four-way entry non-reversible 1,000 mm x 1,200 mm Standard Pallet
This is the most common type of pallet and can be lifted by most lift truck types. It can be lifted by entering on both the narrow edge and the wide edge. When entering on the narrow edge, be aware of the extended load centre and possible de-rating of the lift truck's capacity.

When operating pallet movers and low level order pickers ensure the castor wheels and forks legs are not caught between the boards as this could damage the pallet when lifted.

Pedestrian pallet stackers are not suitable when using this style of pallet as the pallet will be damaged when lifted.

Four-way entry non-reversible, 800 mm x 1,200 mm 'Euro Pallet'
This pallet can be lifted using any truck type that enters from the narrow edge (no boards below to foul the rollers). Rider operated counterbalance or reach trucks and straddle stackers (but not support arm stackers) can enter from wide edge.

The pallet can be lifted by pallet movers or low-level order pickers where the rollers on the legs are not sitting on one of the bearer boards.

Different loads

Intermediate bulk container (IBC)
Used for the transportation of fluids and other bulk materials. These containers are usually cubic and made of plastic, steel or stainless steel.

Flexible intermediate bulk container (big bag, or bulk bag)
Used for the transportation of dry products such as sand, fertiliser, etc. Such bags are composed of thick woven polyethylene or polypropylene and have a capacity of approximately 1,000 kg. They can be lifted on a pallet or by their fitted loops (bags may be single loop or four loop). The single loop is useful for one person operations (no need for a second person to place the loops on the forks). Where a second person is required care must be taken to ensure she or he never place fingers between the loop and the forks.

Corner post pallets/stillages
Composed of metal with either solid
or wire mesh sides. There is a limit on
how high they can be safely stacked.
Ensure that you are aware of the limit
and never exceed it.

Racking system

Pallet racking is a material storage
system which is designed to store
materials on pallets or skids. There
are a variety of pallet racks available.
All enable the storage of materials on
pallets in horizontal rows at multiple
levels, thus increasing storage density.
Pallet racks are a vital and ever
present feature of nearly all modern
warehouses and manufacturing and
distribution facilities.

Always inspect the racking
before use and never exceed the
Safe Working Load (SWL). Only use
pallets that are in good condition.
Read the manufacturer's manual for
racking specifications, components
and inspection requirements.

Racking systems must be inspected regularly to ensure pallets are stacked correctly and checked for damage.

Ensure:
➡ Uprights are secure and undamaged;
➡ Cross members are in good condition and undamaged;
➡ Securing pins are in place;
➡ Pallets are positioned correctly;
➡ Pallets are in good condition and any damaged pallets removed;
➡ Loose items (e.g., boxes) are secured on the pallet (shrink wrapped);
➡ Any defects or damage is reported immediately to a supervisor.

Ensure uniform distribution of the loads by evenly spacing them on the racks.

X.
GENERAL OPERATING PRACTICE

Parking and Travelling Positions

Parking position
Fork tips touching the ground with fork heels as low to the ground as possible.

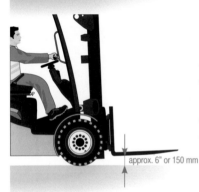

approx. 6" or 150 mm

Travelling position
With the heels of the fork-arms approximately 6 inches (150mm) off the ground and the mast slightly tilted back.

Travelling with a load
With the fork-arms fully inserted lift the load from 4–6 inches (100–150mm) off the ground and apply sufficient back tilt.

Remember, the type of load and ground conditions can affect the stability of the load so adjust your tilt as necessary.

Negotiating Inclines – Unladen

When travelling up an incline without a load you should reverse (forks trailing). This will increase the traction and adhesion of the drive wheels.

When travelling down an incline without a load you should drive forwards (forks leading). This will increase the traction and adhesion of the drive wheels.

When approaching an incline it may be necessary to stop and adjust the height of the fork-arms. Raise them sufficiently to clear the angle of the slope. When you are back on a level surface, lower them to the travel position

Negotiating Inclines – Laden

When travelling down an incline with a load you should reverse (forks/load trailing). This will increase truck and load stability.

When travelling up an incline with a load you should drive forward (forks/load leading). This will increase truck and load stability.

When travelling up an incline with a load that obscures your view you should drive forward with the aid of a banksman to guide you.

Loading & Unloading Vehicles use of Ramps

Loading a vehicle

It is common to begin loading at the front of the vehicle and work towards the rear, loading alternate sides of the vehicle. Ensure items to be unloaded first are loaded last for ease of delivery. Ensure pallets are loaded as tightly as possible to prevent movement during transportation. Load alternate sides to avoid pushing a load across from one side to the other.

Loading from the ground

Inspect the ground around the trailer for holes, manhole covers etc before loading. Ensure that there is sufficient access on both sides of the vehicle, the trailer wheels are chocked and the engine of the vehicle is switched off. Ensure the driver is a safe distance away before loading. When loading curtain-sided trailers ensure the curtain is secured (i.e. tied back).

Unloading a vehicle from the ground

It is common to begin unloading at the rear of the vehicle and work towards the cab. Before unloading, ensure that there is sufficient access on both sides of the vehicle. Inspect the ground for holes, manhole covers etc. Unload from alternate sides (unloading from one side at a time may cause the vehicle trailer to become unstable). Where a pedestrian controlled truck is used ensure that it is set to pedestrian mode for loading or unloading.

When loading from a loading bay ensure that the vehicle's brakes are engaged and wheels chocked. Ensure the bridge plates and trailer floor are capable of sustaining the weight of the forklift and the load. Also ensure the bridge plates are fixed securely. Drive in and out of trailers with caution. When using a mobile ramp ensure it is secured to the goods vehicle correctly. Ensure the lorry driver is in a safe place when loading or unloading goods vehicles.

Stacking Counterbalance

Operators should observe the following basic rules for stacking.

Approach the receiving stack square-on and from a central position. Stop within 6 inches (150mm) of the stack. This will prevent other traffic and pedestrians from passing between the stack and the forks. Apply the handbrake and put the vehicle in neutral. Adjust the tilt to achieve a slight back tilt (the 'stability tilt').

6" or 150 mm

Check for oncoming traffic and look upwards for overhead obstructions. Raise the load to the required height. The underside of the load needs to be approximately 3–5 inches (75–125mm) higher than the receiving stack.

Move forward slowly to ensure accurate alignment as you drive towards the stack. Beware of touching the base of the stack with the base of the mast. Stop when the base of the mast is approximately 4 inches (100mm) from the stack and apply the handbrake. The load will look like it needs to go further forward but do not be tempted to go any closer for if you make contact with the stack it may collapse.

Bring the load level by careful and controlled use of the tilt lever. As you bring the load level it will also go down so be careful to avoid touching the top of the stack. Ensure the load is aligned accurately on all sides of the stack.

Lower the load onto the stack, but also make sure that the stack can cope with extra weight. Ensure the forks are free of the pallet.

Remember, as the weight comes off the fork-arms the forks will flex up, creating a backward tilt. Make sure you adjust the tilt accordingly so as not to drag the load off the top of the stack.

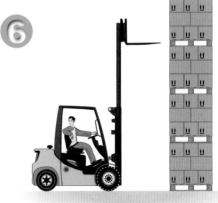

Before moving off, ensure the way is clear. Select reverse, remove parking brake and withdraw from the window of the pallet. Stop when the tips of the forks are no more than 6 inches (150mm) clear of the stack. Apply the handbrake, check the area is clear and lower the fork-arms.

7

Remember, if the mast is tilted back slightly the gap between the tips and the stack will reduce and the risk of touching the stack will increase.

8

Set the fork-arms into the travel position. Select reverse gear, check all around, release the brake and move away looking in the direction of travel.

De-stacking Counterbalance

Operators should observe the following basic rules for de-stacking.

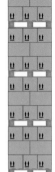

Approach the stack in the correct
travel position (forks 5–6 inches
(125–150mm) off the ground and
slightly tilted back). Slow down
and stop the truck approximately
6 inches (150mm) from the stack.
This will prevent pedestrians from
passing between the fork tips and
the stack as well as assisting with
accurate adjustment of the fork-
arms for entry into the pallet window.

Apply the parking brake and put
vehicle in neutral. This will ensure
truck security and stability and allow
the operator to concentrate on the
hydraulic operation. Bring the mast
to the vertical position (fork-arms level).
Check surroundings and lift the fork-
arms, watching the tips and highest
moving part (backrest or top of mast).

To check the fork-arms are level stop
when the fork-arms are in line with
your eyes. If you need to adjust the
tilt then this would be the ideal time
to do so. Once the forks-arms are
level continue lifting to the required
height to enter the load.

Select forward gear, check surroundings again and release the brake. Moving forward ensure the fork-arms do not rub the pallet boards as this could dislodge the load and the stack could collapse. If necessary adjust the height of the fork-arms (but remember to stop and secure the lift truck before using the hydraulics). As you enter the load you will need to be aware of the backrest extension and the base of the mast so as not to make contact with either overhead obstructions or the base of the stack. Fully enter and heel the load.

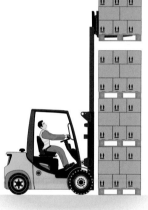

Once the load is heeled apply the parking brake and put the vehicle in neutral. Lift the load to clear the stack. If the load is heavy the fork-arms may flex forward, so adjust as necessary.

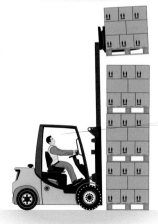

Apply slight back tilt to stabilise the load.
    Remember, as you apply a backward tilt the front of the load will increase in height and the backrest will move backwards. Take care not to touch the stack.

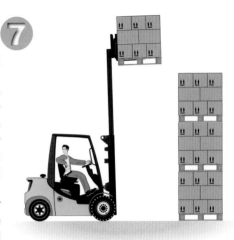

Engage reverse gear, look all around and then release the brake. Reverse the lift truck, looking in the direction of travel, and occasionally check the load is still clear of the stack. Ensure you are sufficiently clear of the face of the stack, then stop, apply the handbrake and engage neutral gear.

Remember, when you lower the load the space between the load and the stack will be reduced by the backward tilt of the mast.

Before lowering the load, check surroundings for oncoming traffic. Do not allow pedestrians or lift trucks to pass under raised loads/fork-arms. Lower the load, making sure that you continue to look around, that the front of the load does not come into contact with the stack and that other traffic does not pass.

Stacking Reach Truck

Reach Truck
In addition to normal forklift operating procedures the guidelines listed below should always be followed:

➡ Never travel with the reach mechanism extended;

➡ Never use the hydraulic controls unless the machine is stopped with the brakes on;

➡ Never let anybody on the straddle legs;

➡ Never place any of your limbs between the mast and the power unit;

➡ Never use the reach mechanism to push or drag loads into position;

➡ Always ensure that the load is lifted above the straddle legs before retracting the load;

➡ Always carry the load on the forks and not on the straddle legs.

Approach the receiving stack square-on and from a central position. Stop within 6 inches (150mm) of the stack. This will prevent other traffic and pedestrians from passing between the stack and forks. Apply the handbrake and put the vehicle into neutral. Adjust the tilt to achieve a slight back tilt (the stability tilt).

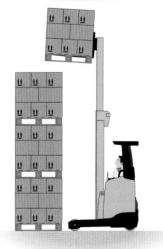

Check for oncoming traffic and look upwards for overhead obstructions. Raise the load to the required height. The underside of the load needs to be approximately 3 to 5 inches (75–125mm) higher than the receiving stack. Drive slowly forward and stop when the reach legs are approximately 2–3 inches (50–75mm) from the stack. Apply the handbrake and select neutral gear.

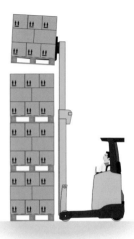

Push the load forward over the top of the receiving stack.

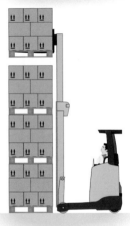

Bring the mast to the vertical position, making allowance for the weight of the load (the heavier the load the more forward flex there will be). Check that the load is aligned on all sides.

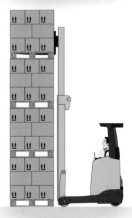

Lower the load onto the top of the stack having ensured that the stack can cope with the weight of the extra load. Check that the forks are free of the pallet. Remember, as the weight comes off the fork-arms the forks will flex up creating a backward tilt. Make sure you adjust the tilt accordingly so as not to drag the load off the top of the stack.

Draw the mast back, while making sure that the fork-arms do not rub the boards of the pallet. Select reverse gear, check all around, and release the brake. Drive in reverse, until the tips of the fork-arms are clear of the stack; stop, apply the handbrake and select neutral gear.

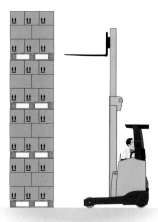

Remember, if the mast is tilted back slightly, the gap between the tips and the stack will reduce as you lower the fork-arms and the risk of touching the stack will increase. Before lowering the fork-arms check all around for oncoming traffic. Do not allow other traffic and pedestrians to pass under the raised fork-arms. Set the fork-arms into the travel position. Select reverse gear, check all around, release the brake and move away looking in the direction of travel.

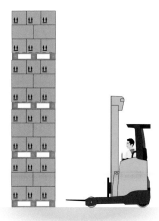

De-stacking Reach Truck

Operators should observe the following basic rules for de-stacking.

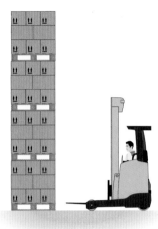

Approach the stack in the correct travel position (forks 5–6 inches (125–150mm) off the ground and slightly tilted back).

Slow down and stop the truck approximately 6 inches (150mm) from the stack. This will prevent other traffic and pedestrians from passing between the fork tips and the stack as well as assisting with accurate adjustment of the fork-arms for entry into the pallet window.

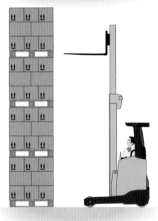

Apply the parking brake and select neutral. This will ensure truck security and stability, and allow the operator to concentrate on the hydraulic operation Bring the mast to the vertical position (fork-arms level). Check all around and lift the fork-arms, watching the tips and highest moving part (the backrest or top of the mast).

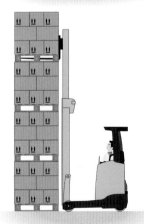

Select forward gear, check all around and move forward until the legs of the lift truck are near but not touching the stack.

Apply the parking brake and select neutral gear. Move the mast forward until the heels of the fork-arms touch the pallet/load. Ensure you do not rub the pallet boards as the forks enter as this could cause the stack to become unstable.

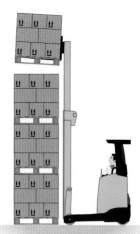

Once the load is heeled, apply the parking brake and select neutral gear. Lift the load to clear the stack. If the load is heavy the fork-arms may flex forward, so adjust, using back tilt as necessary.

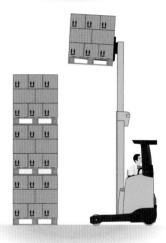

Draw the mast back as far as it will go. Engage reverse gear, look all around and release the brake. Reverse the lift truck, looking in the direction of travel, but checking occasionally that the load is still clear of the stack. Ensure you are sufficiently clear of the face of the stack, then stop, apply the handbrake and engage neutral gear.

Remember, when you lower the load the space between the load and the stack will narrow because of the backward tilt of the mast.

Before lowering the load check all around for oncoming traffic. Do not allow pedestrians or lift trucks to pass under the raised load/fork-arms. Lower the load, making sure you continue to look around, that the front of the load does not come into contact with the stack and that other traffic waits before passing. Lower the load, making sure the load does not land on the reach legs. If it does the pallet may collapse.

Stacking Side Loader

With the load placed securely on the deck of the lift truck, approach the stack with an adequate separation distance of approximately 2–3 inches (50– 75mm) and ensure the lift truck is parallel to the stack.

Once the load is in position, stop the truck, apply the brake and select neutral gear. Lower the stabilising jacks (if the truck has them). Reduce the tilt, bringing the load to a level position.

Raise the load to a height sufficient to ensure that the bottom of the pallet is above the stack.

Move the load out to the point where it is held over the stack.

Lower the load onto the stack. Ensure the load is level in order to maintain the stability of the stack. Adjust the fork-arms to ensure they withdraw cleanly from the pallet.

Bring the mast back while avoiding rubbing the pallet/load as this can cause the stack to become less stable and increase the risk of it collapsing.

Lower the forks to the travel position just below the deck of the lift truck (within chassis height). Raise the stabilising jacks (if the truck has them). Select gear, check all around and release the handbrake. As you drive away from the stack use minimum steering to avoid wheel contact with the stack.

De-stacking – Side Loader

Stop in line with and parallel to the face of the stack. Ensure the gap between the lift truck and the stack is approximately 2–3 inches (50–75mm). Apply the handbrake and select neutral gear. Lower the stabilising jacks (if the vehicle has them). Bring the mast into the vertical position.

Raise the fork-arms and as they pass eye level check to make sure the fork-arms are level. If they are tilted forward as they rise, the tips may come into contact with the stack. Stop when the fork-arms are at the correct height to enter the window of the load.

Carefully move the mast out until the heels of the fork-arms gently touch the load as excessive pressure on the stack could cause it to spring forward as the load is lifted which in turn could make contact with adjacent stacks and cause them to collapse.

Once the load has been lifted clear of the stack, apply slight back tilt to secure and stabilise the load.

Draw the mast back and ensure the load is clear of the stack.

Watch the front of the load as you lower the load down onto the deck of the lift truck. Ensure you do not lower the fork-arms too much and break the underside of the pallet. Raise the stabilising jacks (if the vehicle has them). Select forward gear, check all around, release the handbrake and drive away from the stack. Remember to use minimum steering so as to avoid contact with the stack.

Stacking Pivot Steer Truck

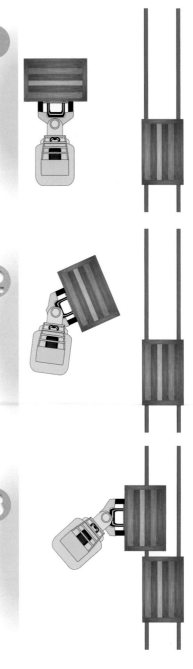

The following procedures for stacking and de-stacking with an articulated lift truck are designed for aisles constructed specifically for this type of lift truck. When operating in open areas, however, follow the procedures for a counter balance or reach truck.

Position the lift truck on the opposite side of the aisle with a clearance of approximately 6 inches (150mm) and stop when the centre of the front wheel is in line with the centre of the space or load.

WITHOUT applying brakes, steer the load towards the racking. As the front corner of the load approaches the face of the stack, engage reverse gear, check your surroundings and slowly reverse the lift truck, continuing to steer until a full lock is applied and then engage the handbrake and select neutral gear. This method will bring the load in line with the space in which it will be deposited more accurately and will allow easier entry into the space.

Reduce the tilt and adjust the height of the load to the space where the load will be placed. Engage gear, look all around and release the brake (G.O.B.). Move forward slowly, adjusting the steering as you move the load into position. Ensure the load is parallel with the side of the racking or stacked pallet.

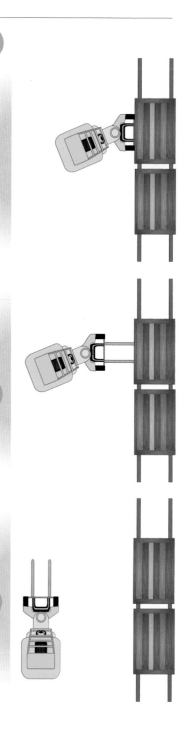

4

As you are entering the pallet space ensure the spaces either side of the load are
equal an make sure the top of the load
and backrest extension do not come into
contact with any overhead obstruction
and the base of the mast does not touch
the racking or load at ground level. Then
stop, apply the handbrake and engage
neutral gear. At this point the load will need
to be levelled; ensure the overhang of the
load is sufficient on both the front and
the back edges (approximately 3 inches
(150mm)). Gently lower the load onto
the racking beams, allowing the beams
to take the weight of the load. Adjust the
fork-arms so they are clear of the pallet.
When bulk stacking and free stacking ensure the load is positioned flush on all four
edges of the receiving stack.

5

Engage reverse gear, check your surroundings and release the handbrake
(G.O.B). Move slowly back and adjust
the steering so the fork-arms stay parallel to the pallet window. Once the tips
of the forks are clear of the stack (approximately 6 inches (150mm)), apply
the handbrake and engage neutral gear.
Check all around and lower the fork-
arms and set them for travel.

6

Engage reverse gear, check all around
and release the handbrake (G.O.B).
As you move the lift truck adjust the
steering to straighten the lift truck. You
are now ready to collect the next load.

De-stacking Pivot Steer Truck

Position the lift truck on the opposite side of the aisle with a clearance of approximately 6 inches (150mm); stop when the centre of the front wheel is in line with the centre of the space or load.

WITHOUT applying brakes, turn towards the racking. As the fork-arms approach the face of the stack, engage reverse gear, check your surroundings and slowly reverse the lift truck, continuing to steer until a full lock is applied and then apply the handbrake and select neutral gear. This method will bring the fork-arms more accurately in line with the space from which the load is going to be collected and will allow easier entry into the pallet window.

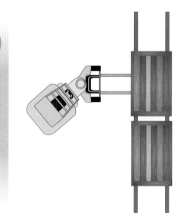

Reduce the tilt and adjust the height of the fork-arms to that of the window of the pallet to be collected. Engage gear, check your surroundings and release the brake (G.O.B). Move forward, slowly, adjusting the steering as necessary. As you move the fork-arms into the window of the pallet adjust the steering to keep the fork-arms in a central position and parallel with the pallet window.

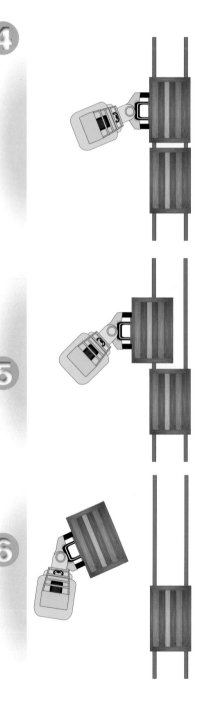

④ Stop when the heels are gently touching the pallet, apply the handbrake and engage neutral gear. Check to ensure the forks are pointed at the centre of the load and that there are no obstructions which might prevent you from lifting the load safely.

Remember to assess the load before lifting, as the weight of the load can affect the stability of the lift truck and that pushing against the load when entering the pallet can cause the load/mast to spring forward as you lift the load. This in turn can cause other loads to be dislodged from their position on the racking especially when back to back racking is in use. Lift the load just clear of the racking shelf and, if there is enough space above the load, apply slight back tilt for load stability.

⑤ Engage gear, check your surroundings and release the handbrake (G.O.B.). Reverse the lift truck, watching both back and front. Apply steering as required to keep the load as straight as possible when withdrawing the load from the space. Side-shift can be used to assist when withdrawing the load from the racking space.

⑥ Once the load is clear of the racking, stop the lift truck, apply the handbrake and select neutral gear. Lower the load with care, ensuring you do not touch the stack with the moving load. You may need to straighten the lift truck to ensure you have enough room to lower the load.

When the load is in the travel position, straighten the lift truck and you are now ready to deliver the load.

Stacking – Pedestrian Controlled Stacker

1

Walk to the stacking area in the safe travel position with the fork-arms leading. Ensure the fork-arms are central to the space. Stop with the front of the load at a distance of 6 inches (150mm) from the racking/stacking area.

2

Ensure the brake is applied by positioning the tiller arm in the fully up or fully down position. Ensure that there is sufficient clear headroom prior to lifting. Lift the load ensuring that the bottom of the pallet is above the racking or bulk stack.

3

Check all around for pedestrians and vehicles. Release the brake by bringing the tiller arm to the correct height to travel. Move forward carefully and if required adjust the steering so that the pallet is positioned correctly.

When stacking in racking, the pallet should be positioned with an equal gap on each side and an overhang to the front of the racking beam. For bulk stacking ensure the load is placed exactly on top of the load underneath. The stack must be upright and level to ensure stability.

Ensure the tiller arm is in full brake applied position. Carefully lower the load. Ensure that the forks are at a height sufficient to clear the pallet as they are withdrawn.

Check all around for pedestrians and vehicles. Ensure that the tiller arm is at the correct height to travel. Walk and face the direction of travel (walking the dog) with the pallet truck following. Occasionally check to ensure that the forks do not touch on the pallet when withdrawing. If there is a risk the fork-arms might rub on withdrawal then stop, apply the brake (tiller arm fully up/down) and adjust as necessary. When the tips of the fork-arms are clear of the stack, approximately 6 inches (150mm), stop and apply the brake.

Check all around and lower the fork-arms to the travel position.

De-stacking – Pedestrian Controlled Stacker

Approach the stack with the fork-arms leading and positioned towards the centre of the load to be collected. Stop approximately 6 inches (150mm) from the face of the stack.

Apply the brake position (tiller arm fully up/down). Adjust the height of the fork-arms to enter the window of the pallet.

Check your surroundings for pedestrians and vehicles. Release the brake by bringing the tiller arm to the correct height for travel. Then, moving forward carefully, adjust the steering until the fork heels just touch the pallet.

If when entering the pallet window there is a risk the fork-arms may rub, stop, apply the brake and adjust fork-arms as required.

When the fork-arms are fully inserted in the load, stop and apply the brake. Check surroundings, including above you for overhead obstructions, and lift the pallet just clear of the stack. Apply slight back tilt if possible to stabilise the load.

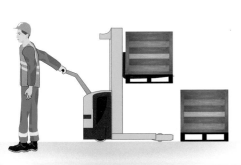

Check around you for pedestrians and vehicles. Ensure that the tiller arm is at the correct height to travel. Move backwards, ensuring that you walk and look in the direction of travel. Check occasionally that the pallet/load is not coming into contact with the racking or adjacent stacks as you withdraw it. Adjust the steering as required to prevent this. When the load is clear of the stack (6 inches (150mm)) stop and apply the brake.

With the brake applied, lower the load to the safe travel position. You are now ready to deliver the load. Ensure when travelling with a pedestrian powered truck that you always walk facing the direction of travel; taking backward steps can lead to the operator tripping, being run over or even pinned against a wall or another object.

Picking Up – Powered Pallet Truck

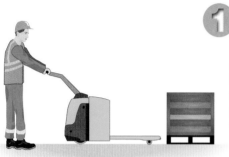

Approach the stack with the fork-arms leading and positioned towards the centre of the load to be collected. Stop approximately 6 inches (150mm) from the face of the stack.

Apply the brake position (tiller arm fully up/down). Adjust the height of the fork-arms to enter the window of the pallet.

Check your surroundings for pedestrians and other traffic; then bring the tiller arm to the correct position for travel and enter the load. When the fork-arms have gone far enough into the pallet stop and put the truck into the brake position. It might not be possible to fully enter all loads as the fork-arms might be longer than the load. The position of the castor wheels will need to be taken into account. If they are on top of the pallet board when the load is lifted the pallet will break.

With the brake applied, lift the load clear of the ground. Then assess the ground conditions before moving off.

Check your surroundings for pedestrians and other traffic. Position the tiller arm correctly for travel and then start to move at walking pace and facing in the direction of travel.

Setting Down – Powered Pallet Truck

With the load leading, walk towards the pallet set-down area in the safe travel position. When the load is in the correct position, stop and apply the brake.

With the tiller arm in the brake applied position lower the load to the ground carefully. Ensure the forks are at a height which will allow them to clear the pallet when withdrawing.

Check your surroundings for pedestrians and other traffic and then adjust the tiller arm to the correct position for travel. Walking and looking in the opposite direction, slowly withdraw the fork-arms from the window of the pallet. Check from time to time that the fork-arms are withdrawing cleanly. Stop when the tips of the fork-arms are approximately 6 inches (150mm) clear of the pallet.

With the brake applied, set the fork-arms into the safe travel position.

Check your surroundings for pedestrians and other traffic. Set the tiller arm to the correct height for travel and move off at walking pace, looking in the direction of travel.

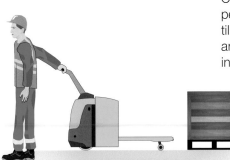

Stacking – VNA

With the lift truck set correctly for operating within the aisle, travel along the aisle until you reach the desired stacking location. Diagonal travel may be used when recommended by the manufacturer. Read the operator's manual for guidance before you use the diagonal travel applications for the first time.

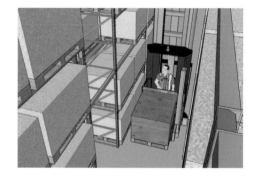

When the desired stacking location has been reached, stop the lift truck. Check above you for overhead obstructions and lift the cab to ensure that you have a clear view of the space being filled.

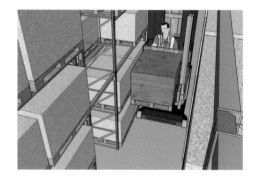

Lift the load, using the secondary lift mechanism, to a height allowing the underneath of the load to clear the racking beam.

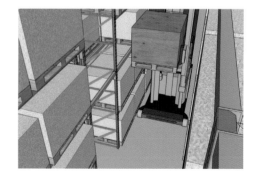

Check to ensure the load is in line with the space to be filled. Move the load out to place it in the racking. Ensure the load is correctly positioned (i.e. that there is equal space on either side of the load and the face of the load is in line with the other loads in the racking).

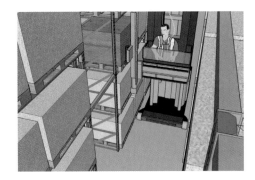

Using the secondary lift mechanism, lower the load on to the racking beam. Ensure the fork-arms are clear of the pallet to prevent rubbing. Move the forks in fully to the 'home' position.

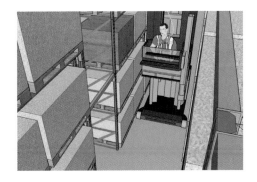

Lower the fork-arms using the secondary lift mechanism. Before lowering the cab check below for pedestrians and obstructions. Lower the cab to the safe travel height where you are ready to collect the next load.

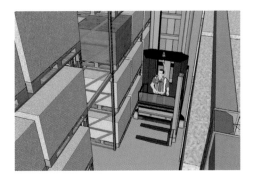

De-stacking – VNA

Travel along the aisle until you reach the desired location.

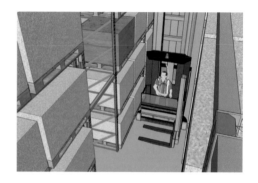

Check overhead for obstructions. Raise the cab to the required height, so that your eyes are level with the window of the pallet.

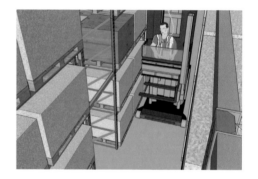

Using the secondary lift mechanism, raise the fork-arms to the window of the pallet. Ensure the fork-arms are set for clean entry.

Move the fork-arms out to enter the pallet window. Stop when the load is heeled correctly.

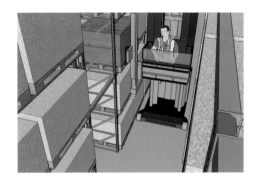

Using the secondary lift mechanism, lift the load far enough to clear the racking beam. Move the fork-arms in as far as the home position. Lower the load using the secondary lift mechanism. Remember, travelling with the load higher than the cab screen could lead to the load spilling into the cab and injuring the operator.

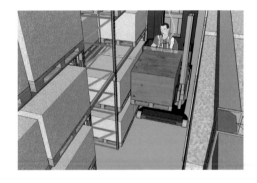

Before lowering the cab check below for pedestrians and obstructions. Lower the cab and load to the safe travel height. Check that the aisle is clear of obstructions and if pedestrians are in the aisle ask them to leave it before moving off.

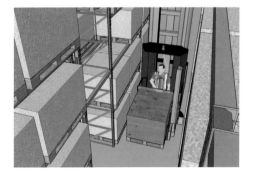

XI.
LIFT TRUCK ATTACHMENTS

The following pictures show various types of attachment for use on various types of load. When using an attachment consider the following:

➡ **Is the correct attachment being used?**
➡ **How will the attachment affect the overall dimensions of the lift truck?**
➡ **How will the attachment affect the load centre distance and how will that affect the lift truck's rated capacity?**

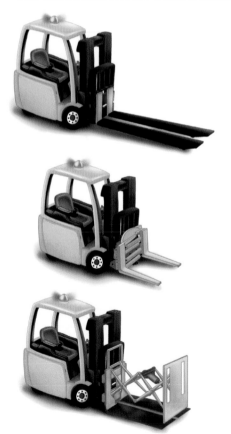

Fork extensions:
Used to carry large loads that would normally tip on a standard fork-arm.

The lift truck is longer and will have a reduced capacity.

Fork spreader:
Allows the operator to adjust the spread of the fork-arms without leaving the confines of the lift truck.

The lift truck's rated capacity will need to match the weight of the attachment.

Slip sheet:
Enables the operator to collect and deposit loads without pallets being used.

Reduces the maximum rated capacity of the lift truck and may increase the load centre.

Double deep fork extension:
Allows the operator to stack loads into double deep racking systems.

The rated capacity will be greatly reduced when forks are extended.

Pallet/load rotator:
Allows the pallet or load to be inverted.

Reduces the maximum capacity of the lift truck.

**Barrel clamp
(manual operation):**
Allows the operator to carry cylindrical loads (e.g., barrels).

Load centre will be extended, capacity reduced and the overall length of the lift truck increased, increases the load centre.

Cylindrical carrying platform:
Enables the operator to carry cylindrical loads that could not be transported using a barrel clamp.

Paper/whitegoods clamp:
Used to collect and transport bales of paper and white goods (e.g., washing machines, fridges etc).

Twin fork-arm attachment:
Allows two pallet loads to be carried at the same time.

Lift trucks with a greater capacity are normally used with this attachment.

Barrell/keg clamp:
Used to collect and transport multiple barrels or kegs.

Has reduced capacity, extended load centre and reduced visibility.

Man-up platform:
Rated capacity reduced by 50%. Allows a person to be lifted to access high areas that normally cannot be reached.

This attachment should only be used in exceptional circumstances. Personnel must not be transported while in the platform. Before use the operator and personnel in the platform will need to be given specific job training.

Boom attachment:
Used to collect and transport long cylindrical loads (e.g., carpets).

This will increase the overall length of the lift truck. Therefore the load centre distance will also increase and the lifting capacity of the lift truck will reduce.

Crane jib attachment:
Used to lift loads not normally carried on a pallet or loads that may need to be positioned over a working area (e.g., engines being removed from or fitted to a vehicle).

Hopper:
Used to collect, transport and deposit loads into piles or hoppers (e.g., sand, soil, pee shingle, grain, etc.)

Side-shift:
Fitted to the majority of modern lift trucks, this attachment will assist the operator to accurately stack loads and keep the weight distributed evenly on the fork-arms. It also assists the operator when stacking loads tightly together and will reduce damage to the product.

ADDITIONAL SAFETY RULES

Rules for Operators of Tractor –Trailer Equipment

1. Undertake pre-operational check (tyres etc).
2. Ensure the trailer load is secured correctly and safely positioned. Never overload a trailer or load unevenly. Ensure the tow-bar is secured.
3. Always allow for corner cutting of the trailer when negotiating a turn.
4. Extra care is required when transporting an extra wide load. Ensure you have sufficient clearance on both sides.
5. Extra care is required when reversing: never reverse ‚blind' (i.e. when your view is obstructed by the load always get help to assist in the manoeuvre).
6. Always, where more than one trailer is being towed, drive down gradients slowly to ensure trailers do not crash into one another.
7. Never exceed the rated towing capacity.
8. Always operate equipment as per your training.

Rules for Operators of Lateral and Front Stacking Trucks

1. Carry out the pre-operational check.
2. Check aisle is free of obstacles.
3. Stack safely and correctly, and ensure the load overhang is level.
4. Report any dangerous movement of a load.
5. Exercise care when placing a load on to the racking. Never allow the fork-arms to come in contact with the racking.
6. Always stack and destack as per your training and adhere to speed restrictions. Ensure the forks are fully inserted into each pallet to be stacked or destacked.
7. Do not operate trucks over gradients unless the truck is designed for such operations.
8. Always carry loads correctly and safely and never attempt to transport a load by pushing or dragging with the forklift or any forklift attachments.
9. Always remain vigilant for other vehicles or pedestrians in the aisles.
10. Inspect the load prior to lifting. If the load is unsuitable do not lift it and contact your supervisor.
11. Never carry passengers.
12. Keep hands/arms and feet/legs inside the cab.
13. Before lifting ensure the fork-arms are fully inserted into the pallet.

Rules for Diesel and Petrol Refuelling

1. Refuel in designated area(s) only.
2. Wear appropriate PPE gloves, overalls, safety glasses, etc.
3. Ensure fire extinguisher is close to hand.
4. Never smoke or use naked flame in the refuelling area.
5. Do not use a mobile phone in the refuelling area.
6. Use the designated vessels for refuelling only.
7. Always ensure the truck engine is off before refuelling.
8. Ensure the correct fuel is used.
9. Clean up any spillages immediately.
10. Never overfill the tank.
11. Ensure the cap is replaced securely.
12. Never mix petrol or blended fuels with diesel.

Rules for Liquefied Petroleum Gas (LPG) Refuelling

1. Only trained and competent persons may undertake refuelling.
2. Change the LPG cylinder out of doors whenever possible.
3. Refuel in designated area only.
4. Ensure you are familiar with the LPG supplier's instructions for safe filling, use and storage of LPG cylinders.
5. Never smoke or use naked flames or any other source of heat in the refuelling area.
6. Ensure the engine is turned off BEFORE disconnecting the gas cylinder.
7. Inspect cylinder parts (i.e. sealing washers, threads, hose couplings, etc). Ensure all parts are free of damage. Report damage immediately to your supervisor.
8. Ensure the cylinder valve and hose couplings are tightened sufficiently.
9. Ensure the cylinder is fitted in its cradle correctly (read manufacturer's manual).
10. Always handle fuel cylinders carefully at all times.
11. Never attempt to adjust carburetor equipment or ignition system in the event the truck fails to start after changing the cylinder.
12. Report any failed starts to your supervisor immediately.
13. Never park the forklift truck next to a source of heat such as a radiator. Never park the forklift truck with its gas cylinder in line with the exhaust unit of another ,ticking over' parked forklift truck.
14. Turn off the cylinder valve when the truck is not operating.
15. Park in designated areas only. NEVER park adjacent to open pits, lift shafts etc. ALWAYS obey parking restrictions.
16. Never use a damaged or leaking cylinder. Any damaged or leaking cylinder should be taken to a safe area away from sources of ignition. Report damaged or leaking cylinders immediately to your supervisor.

XIII.
APPENDIX
SAFETY SIGN

Safety Signage

All places of work will display some type (s) of safety signage. The Safety, Health and Welfare at Work (General Application) Regulations 2007 (specifically Chapter 1 Part 9 and Schedule 9) state the requirements for safety signs and signals. This section does not deal with acoustic signs, verbal communication, hand signals, signage in relation to dangerous substances/preparations/products or equipment. The above regulations should be read in conjunction with this chapter.

A sign is an object which provides specific information/instructions via its geometric shape, specific colours and use of a specific symbol or pictogram. The purpose of the sign is to give information/instructions without using text.

Safety signage is used in the workplace where hazards cannot be avoided or sufficiently reduced, and it is the duty of the employer to provide these safety or health signs as per the regulations above. Appropriate signage must be placed at relevant positions for emergency routes and exits, fire fighting equipment, areas at risk from falling objects and/or risk of falling a distance, traffic routes, risk of exposure to noise, etc. The type of signage used must be in accordance with Part 7, Chapter 1 of the Regulations.

Types of Signage

There are a number of different types of sign and each has its own specific meaning. Types of sign include; Prohibition, Fire Fighting, Warning, Mandatory, Emergency Escape/First Aid and Supplementary signs. A Supplementary sign is used in conjunction with another sign. This sign provides supplementary information and they are the same colour as the main sign it accompanies. A directional arrow is an example of a supplementary sign.

Each of the signs listed above have specific recognisable features as follows:

Prohibition signs

Prohibition signs are round in their geometric shape. They are red with black pictogram on white background. This sign means that a specific act or behaviour is prohibited. Examples of prohibition signs;

General prohibition sign

No smoking

No open flame; Fire, open ignition source and smoking prohibited

No thoroughfare

Not drinking water

No access for forklift trucks and other industrial vehicles

Do not touch

Do not extinguish with water

No heavy load

No activated mobile phones

No pushing

No sitting

No stepping on surface

Do not use lift in the event of fire

No dogs

No eating or drinking

Do not obstruct

Do not walk or stand here

Do not use this lift for people

Mandatory Signs

Mandatory signs are also round in their geometric shape. They are blue with white pictogram. This sign unlike the prohibition sign means the requirement of a specific action e.g. Ear protection must be worn. Examples of mandatory signs;

General mandatory action sign

Refer to instruction manual/booklet

Wear ear protection

Wear eye protection

Wear safety footwear

Wear protective gloves

Wear protective clothing

Wash your hands

Use handrail

Wear a face shield

Wear head protection

Wear high-visibility clothing

Wear respiratory protection

Wear a safety harness

Wear safety belts

Use barrier cream

Use this walkway

Use protective apron

Warning Signs

Warning signs are triangular in their geometric shape. They are yellow with black pictogram. This sign means that a specific hazard or risk is present. Examples of warning signs;

General warning sign

Warning; Explosive material

Warning; Radioactive material or ionising radiation

No Warning; Laser beam

Warning; Non-ionising radiation

Warning; Magnetic field

Warning; Floor level obstacle

Warning; Drop (fall)

Warning; Biological hazard

Warning; Low temperature/freezing conditions

Warning; Slippery surface

Warning; Electricity

Warning; Guard dog

Warning; Warning; Forklift trucks and other industrial vehicles

Warning; Overhead load

Warning; Toxic material

Warning; Hot surface

Warning; Automatic start-up

Warning; Crushing

Warning; Overhead obstacle

Warning;
Flammable
material

Warning; Sharp
element

Warning; Corrosive
substance

Warning;
Crushing of hands

Warning;
Counterrotating rollers

Warning; Battery
charging

Warning; Oxidising
substance

Warning;
Pressurised cylinder

Emergency Escape or First Aid Signs

Emergency escape or first aid signs are rectangular or square in their geometric shape. They are green with white pictogram. These signs show information on emergency exits and illustrate first aid provision and rescue. Examples of emergency escape and first aid signs;

Emergency exit
(left hand)

Emergency exit
(right hand)

First aid

Emergency
telephone

Evacuation
assembly point

Eyewash station

Safety shower

Stretcher

This way
(supplementary
information)

This way
(supplementary
information)

This way
(supplementary
information)

This way
(supplementary
information)

Fire Fighting Signs

Fire fighting signs are also rectangular or square in their geometric shape. They are red with white pictogram. These signs show information on fire fighting equipment and emergency communication. Examples of fire fighting signs;

Fire extinguisher

Fire hose reel

Fire ladder

Collection of firefighting equipment

Fire alarm call point

Fire emergency telephone

This way (supplementary information)

This way (supplementary information)

This way (supplementary information)

This way (supplementary information)

Additional signage

Background white, wording or symbol black
or
Background safety colour, wording or symbol contrasting colour
Symbols must be as simple as practicable and easy to understand.

Yellow/black danger identification

Identification of permanent risk locations such as: steps, holes in floors, etc.
Areas where there is a risk of:

➡ collision
➡ falling
➡ stumbling
➡ falling load

Or where there is a real but unspecified danger.

Packaging Handling Instructions

Packages found within the workplace environment are marked with specific packaging handling and safety instructions by use of pictogram symbol(s). Examples below of some common symbols used on packaging.

This way up

Keep away from water

Fragile

Stacking limit by number

Stacking limit by mass

Do not stack

Protect from radioactive sources

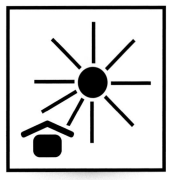

Keep away from sunlight

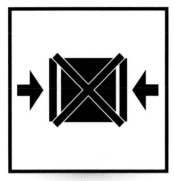

Do not clamp as indicated

Do not use hand hooks

Clamp as indicated

Centre of gravity

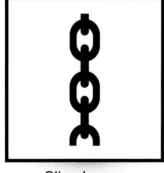

Sling here

Do not roll

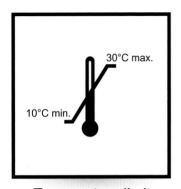

Temperature limits

Do not use hand truck here

Use no forks

Handle with care

Flammable

Heavy load

Recycle

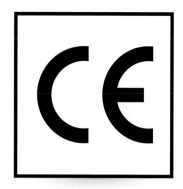

CE Marking

Put litter in bin

Do not open with sharp instrument

AUTHORISATION TO OPERATE LIFT TRUCKS

This is to certify that

is authorised to operate the following Mechanical Handling Equipment

Make	Model	Type	Capacity	Attachment	Expiry Date
			kg's		
			kg's		
			kg's		
			kg's		
			kg's		

In the following areas:

Company premises:	
Designated area(s):	
Other:	

Manager Name:	
Manager Signature:	

Employee Name:	
Employee Signature:	
Key Number:	

Failure to comply with the Companies Safe Operating Procedures may result in the operator having their **authorisation to operate lift trucks** revoked and may be brought in for a disciplinary hearing.

AUTHORISATION TO OPERATE LIFT TRUCKS

This is to certify that the persons listed below are authorised
to operate the following Mechanical Handling Equipment

Make	Model	Type	Capacity	Attachment
			kg's	

Employee Name	Date Tested	Expiry Date	Key Number	Employee signature

In the following areas:

Company premises:	
Designated area(s):	
Other:	

Manager Name:	
Manager Signature:	

Failure to comply with the Companies Safe Operating Procedures may result in the operator having their **authorisation to operate lift trucks** revoked and may be brought in for a disciplinary hearing.

RACKING INSPECTION LOG

It is the responsibility of the employee/contractor to inspect the racking condition and report to the management any damage to the racking as soon as it occurs.

The identification of damage to racking and the severity of damage will be as follows:

➡ The inspection log will be completed in full at regular intervals.

➡ The racking will be marked with a colour coded system which identifies the damage has already been reported to management and action is to be taken. Only when management are satisfied with the repair will the identification label be removed.

Minor damage will be marked with

Damage that will need a second opinion will be marked with

Major damage will be marked with

➡ In the event of major damage the racking MUST be isolated and reported to management immediately. On inspection further action will be taken under supervision of a senior person. DO NOT attempt to fix the problem yourself.

RACKING INSPECTION RECORD

DATE	Anchor Bolts	Uprights	Cross Beams	Locking Pins	Load Position/ Safety	Capacity Chart	Swl Labels	Checked By

TRACTION BATTERY – Specific Gravity reading Log

On electrically powered trucks the specific gravity **(S.G.)** of the traction batteries should be taken and recorded before and after each charge using the table below.

Each table is numbered 1-24 and the cells of the battery should be numbered accordingly. This can be done by simply painting numbers on each cell cap with a small paint brush. (This form can also be used for 36 and 48 cell batteries)

EXAMPLE: On a lift truck with 24 cells, each cell is given a number from 1 to 24. Sample readings are taken and recorded on the chart as shown below. The top reading represents „before charging" and the bottom reading „after charging" and then initialled by the person who carried out the chceck.

Fork Truck – Serial Number: ....

Battery Serial Number: ....

Date of first reading: ....

Date of last reading: ....

Cell number

1 →
| 1.150 | K.P |
| 1.260 | R.P |

Specific gravity before charging

Initials of person checking S.G.

Specific gravity after charging

Initials of person checking S.G.

1		2		3		4	
8		7		6		5	
9		10		11		12	
16		15		14		13	
17		18		19		20	
24		23		22		21	
25		26		27		28	
32		31		30		29	
33		34		35		36	
40		39		38		37	
41		42		43		44	
48		47		46		45	

All cells should be checked within 28 days or by the seventh charge. Specific gravity: **1.280 FULL   1.140 FLAT**

     Form can be downloaded from: **www.hspublications.ie**

RACKING INSPECTION LOG

It is the responsibility of the employee/contractor to inspect the racking condition and report to the management any damage to the racking as soon as it occurs.

The identification of damage to racking and the severity of damage will be as follows:

➡ The inspection log will be completed in full at regular intervals.

➡ The racking will be marked with a colour coded system which identifies the damage has already been reported to management and action is to be taken. Only when management are satisfied with the repair will the identification label be removed.

Minor damage will be marked with

Damage that will need a second opinion will be marked with

Major damage will be marked with

➡ In the event of major damage the racking MUST be isolated and reported to management immediately. On inspection further action will be taken under supervision of a senior person. DO NOT attempt to fix the problem yourself.

RACKING INSPECTION RECORD

DATE	Anchor Bolts	Uprights	Cross Beams	Locking Pins	Load Position/ Safety	Capacity Chart	Swl Labels	Checked By

PRE-USE CHECKLIST (DAILY)

Driver Name:			Date:		Time:
Fork Truck Make/Model/Reg Number:					

Item	N/A	Checked	Detected fault
1. Fork-arms			
2. Carriage Plate/Attachment			
3. Backrest Extension			
4. Mast			
5. Mast Rollers/Slides			
6. Lift Chains			
7. Chain Pulleys			
8. Hydraulics			
9. Wheels			
10. Tyres			
11. External Truck Body			
12. Battery			
13. Operating Position			
14. Capacity Rating Plate			
15. Operator Seat/Seat Belt			
16. Starting Procedure Electric Fork Truck			
17. Starting Procedure Engine Truck			
18. Starting Procedure Gas Powered Truck			
19. Lights/Indicators/Flashing Beacon			
20. Audible Warnings			
21. Hydraulic Controls			
22. Driving/Braking			
23. Steering			
24. Other			
25. Other			

Faults Reported:	☐ Yes ☐ No	Reported to:	Date

     Form can be downloaded from: **www.hspublications.ie**

PRE-USE CHECKLIST (WEEKLY)

Driver Name:					Date:			Time:	

Fork Truck Make/Model/Reg Number:

Item	MON	TUE	WED	THUR	FRI	SAT	SUN	Detected fault
1. Fork-arms								
2. Carriage Plate/Attachment								
3. Backrest Extension								
4. Mast								
5. Mast Rollers/Slides								
6. Lift Chains								
7. Chain Pulleys								
8. Hydraulics								
9. Wheels								
10. Tyres								
11. External Truck Body								
12. Battery								
13. Operating Position								
14. Capacity Rating Plate								
15. Operator Seat/Seat Belt								
16. Starting Procedure Electric Fork Truck								
17. Starting Procedure Engine Truck								
18. Starting Procedure Gas Powered Truck								
19. Lights/Indicators/Flashing Beacon								
20. Audible Warnings								
21. Hydraulic Controls								
22. Driving/Braking								
23. Steering								
24. Other								
25. Other								

Faults Reported: ☐ Yes ☐ No	Reported to:	Date

TRACTION BATTERY – Specific Gravity reading Log

On electrically powered trucks the specific gravity **(S.G.)** of the traction batteries should be taken and recorded before and after each charge using the table below.

Each table is numbered 1-24 and the cells of the battery should be numbered accordingly. This can be done by simply painting numbers on each cell cap with a small paint brush. (This form can also be used for 36 and 48 cell batteries)

EXAMPLE: On a lift truck with 24 cells, each cell is given a number from 1 to 24. Sample readings are taken and recorded on the chart as shown below. The top reading represents „before charging" and the bottom reading „after charging" and then initialled by the person who carried out the chceck.

Fork Truck – Serial Number: ....

Battery Serial Number: ....

Date of first reading: ....

Date of last reading: ....

Cell number

1 | 1.150 K? | Specific gravity before charging
Initials of person checking S.G.
1.260 R.E | Specific gravity after charging
Initials of person checking S.G.

1		2		3		4	
8		7		6		5	
9		10		11		12	
16		15		14		13	
17		18		19		20	
24		23		22		21	
25		26		27		28	
32		31		30		29	
33		34		35		36	
40		39		38		37	
41		42		43		44	
48		47		46		45	

All cells should be checked within 28 days or by the seventh charge. Specific gravity: **1.280 FULL   1.140 FLAT**

126 © Health and Safety Publications 2012

Form can be downloaded from: **www.hspublications.ie**

ACKNOWLEDGEMENT FORM

I acknowledge that I have received training and information (including Fork Truck safety code booklet) regarding the safe and correct operation

Of the following Mechanical Handling Equipment:	
Trainee (print name):	
Trainee Signature:	
Manager Name (if applicable):	
Company name (if applicable):	
Date:	

    Form can be downloaded from: **www.hspublications.ie**